M000198436

Don Quickshot

DON QUICKSHOT

by

William Van Wert

Livingston Press
at
The University of West Alabama

ISBN 0-942979-32-X, paper
ISBN 0-942979-31-1, cloth

Library of Congress Catalog Card Number: 96-77672

Manufactured in the United States of America.

Printed on acid-free paper.
first edition

Typesetting and layout: Joe Taylor, Beth Grant, Lee Holland-Moore
Special thanks for proofreading of foreign languages: Mary Pagliero & Stephen Slimp

For further information on our list of books, please write

Livingston Press
Station 22
The University of West Alabama
Livingston, AL 35470

Other books by the author:

The Film Career of Alain Robbe-Grillet
The Theory and Practice of the Cine-Roman
Tales for Expectant Fathers
The Discovery of Chocolate
Missing in Action
Memory Links
Stool Wives
Proper Myth (forthcoming)

Don Quickshot

for Ian

1.

The Don wore rings on every finger,
the better to check the stars,

or he wore none at all. It didn't matter.
He called them brass knuckles.

The way Little Red Riding Hood
came from vampires, he came from clouds.

We're off to slay a man named Sid,
he told his torpedo Pedro Torres,

whose real name was Lanza or Pinzo
or Panza. It didn't matter.

He was a dimwit slovenly gullible squire.
I know the Sid of whom you speak.

He lives in another time zone.
We'll never catch him.

2.

But we can try. Assay. Go sally forth.
Put quitclaim to this ditchdull

monotony we call a mob. Quest
is the root of every question. Besides,

the shadow can never divest itself
of the one who casts it.

Pedro didn't understand what shadows
had to do with Sid, *sol y sombra*

from sombreros. The Don had ordered
a hit. He would live with that.

Shall I go get the Caddy? Pedro said.
No, the Don replied. Caddy smells like trees.

Any Don can go by car. I have in mind
to go by horse, travel backwards in time,

the incognito thing. Traveler,
I call my steed. You can call yours Spot.

Ay chingao, Pedro said. No offense,
boss, but you're mounted on a mule.

The Don wore rings on every finger,
or he wore none at all. He checked

the stars he called brass knuckles.
For such as he, a horse is a horse

is a horse, of course, and can
easily be a mule. Easily.

Horse, ass, burro, mule,
Tio Toby's hobbyhorse, it doesn't matter,

Don replied. I have no truck
with trivial things. I'll not abide

your quibbling. Call a spade *espada*.
It's the zemblance that counts.

3.

So they set out, headed south,
the Don regaled in epaulettes,

a frock coat like the frothy butlers
wear in Gothic novels,

mounted on a mule, in search of Sid.
With a love that bordered on loyalty

Pedro Torres trailed behind,
not because he believed in a certain

respectful servile distance,
but because Spot was stubborn.

They witnessed things most wonderful:
the pierced ears of virgin women

on the Isla de Mujeres; swinging
monkeys in Belize, banana trees and

jalousies, black gangsters selling smack
who sang like Paul Robeson: enticements

of every carnal sort: Rita Hayworth look-alikes,
but no one who had heard of Sid.

Guatemala was a desert: shifting sand;
hazy Dracula sun spots; no crops;

wandering hordes of refugees,
selling cigarettes for bread.

The Don was not dismayed. He brandished
his sword and sent them packing

like they'd seen a ghost
or trespassed in a bad mirage.

He spake little, but when he spake,
it came out caked with sand.

When the snow covers the frozen lake,
there is still the lake.

4.

Nicaragua like a nightmare.
Sandanistas everywhere. Whole villages

wrapped in concertina, passion play
of crown of thorns. Little children

with machetes. Pregnant mothers
at the well, a bucket in one hand,

machine gun in the other. Starving,
three-legged dogs. Border checks

for *pasaportes*. Accused of being CIA.
Undetained. Dismissed as being lunatics,

undercover *Sixty Minutes*,
runners for the drug cartel.

Embraced by contras in the woods,
who wished to eat their mules.

Encounter with a proverb-master,
wearing camouflage. Sartorial.

*En este mundo de penas y desdicha
casi nadie está contento con su picha.*

What's he say, Pedro?
He say a poem should not mean,

he talk a lot but mean little,
plomo y plata, lead and silver.

I get it. Bullets and ballots. I seen
that film. Does he know Sid?

No, *patron*. Then give him bullets.

5.

"Arena" means sand. This old man came at us, shouting *"Sangre y arena,"* which means "blood and sand." But the Don thought he was talking fight arena, and he had me blow the old man away. "Arena" means sand. Misinterpretations lead to violence every time. Never seen it fail. The old man had a bottle in his hand, but the Don didn't see a bottle. He saw billy-club. That makes ten people he's had me off since we crossed the border.

The Don is crazy. I know it. Sometimes, I forget to pretend not to know it. He's been crazy ever since this dude named Sid did some unforgivable wrong to the Don's moll Dulcie. Dulcie didn't care, but the Don, he took it personal. He wasn't always like this. When I got back from 'Nam, I was the crazy one, and he took a bunch of us in, hired on the spot, and to do the very thing I was good at and trained for, which was and still is hitting. There weren't any other employers waiting in line to do as much.

A thousand people were buried alive with their pharaohs, man. Chinese did the same. I'm not the first dude to take orders from a nut. Maybe we'll find Sid, maybe not. Maybe we'll get back alive, maybe not. I smell like my snotty mule, but I'm not complaining.

I told the Don 'arena' means *sand,* and he said to me: "Do you think the forest recognizes an individual tree?" Wood is wood, I guess.

6.

Honduras like a hunchback.
Mountains for shoulders, head

tucked in to wildflowers. Sunsets
so low they guillotine the trees.

An American in war fatigues,
waiting for them as they crossed the border.

He looked like an emu or clipped bald eagle,
but he walked and talked like a man.

An enumeration of his sew-on patches:
Flying Tigers. Flying Burrito Brothers.

Kick ass, not the bucket.
I'm not fonda Jane.

Da Nang is for lovers. Rocky V.
The squeaky wheel gets greased.

War and turista: they go together.
I fucked Pippi Longstockings.

Mister Trump, from the State Department,
he said in a tin-whinny voice,

but his chaps called him Colonel.
They had bootblack faces

and looked like they'd feasted
on live crow. They used the phrase

'the whole nine yards' in every sentence.
You boys could use fresh mounts, I'd say.

We got a green Huey, take you back
to the US of A. Whaddya say?

The Don replied: Do you know Sid?
An Arab necromancer named Sid Hammett?

Wrong direction, gramps. No A-rabs here.
Then we shall have no truck with you.

Okay, I tried tact. Let's cut to the chase.
What's your scam? Actors? ACLU?

PTL? PLO? Guinness Book of Records?
Muleskinners? What's the skinny?

We search for Sid and chivalry,
both of them lost. The Colonel waved

him off. I'm here to tell you,
off the record, one side or the other,

you can't come down here without
just cause. You can't be killing people.

We do that. Look at yourself.
You give the Salvation Army a bad name.

And those stinking mules. We got a
situation here that I can't let grow

into an incident. You're embarrassing
the Stars and Stripes. Go home

or else, I don't know, watch your backs.
We cannot. The Colonel tried another tack.

Son, he said, ignoring the Don
and squaring Pedro in his sights,

You look like you could use a Big Mac
and some fries about now. Hot shower,

clean sheets, a little tookie.
Take the old man back to pasture,

mothball the coats, all charges dropped.
Whaddya say? Pedro decided to try a proverb:

A torpedo cannot sink a ship
without the hand that fires it.

The Colonel had no proof, no wit,
no real jurisdiction. So he gave up.

I ought to have my men spraypaint
the both of you, cut off your ears,

leave a Sandanista smell. Who would know?
But you guys are bad luck and boomerangs,

and I don't want no Donkeygate.
You can go. Ramon, go with them.

And so, after much debate, with many
moot points, they quit their countryman,

Ramon, on foot behind them.
He had no trouble keeping up.

7.

They passed a king in a horse-drawn
carriage, shades drawn, a surreptitious

surrey, who demanded right of way.
And when the mules wouldn't move,

which was their wont, the king got out
and Pedro slew him. Ramon looked

the other way. He hated aristocracy.
They passed a barber on the road,

wearing his basin on his head.
The Don did all the talking.

Are you from Seville? No, *señor*.
Do you know Sid? No, *señor*.

No lo conozco. Then you must be
a saracen. Kill him, Pedro.

This he did. Kill Ramon too.
This he did. But Ramon got up

and followed them, forehead bleeding.
And thus they entered the pores

of Brobdinags, giant women,
breasts like geodesic domes,

hips as wide as Colorado, hearts
of stone. Pedro was *outré*-aroused.

I want to penetrate your pores,
to be as close as kith and kin,

I want to colonize you.
Handcuff me. I'm yours.

His words were garbled, enveloped
in viscous, amniotic fluids.

They swam in veins for forty days,
as many nights, if not more,

nourished in blood, the frayed ends
of chewed food, kept awake

by the dark growls of indigestion,
a broomcloset of bile and gas,

cilia, tripe the size of boa constrictors,
awash as it were in the rivers of Lethe

with a faint smell of estrogen.
Using pieces of food for rafts,

they dog-paddled down the maelstrom
of sucked descent: inner-tubing

like a coral reef, ghostly gastric
screams of wild dogs and all who had

abandoned hope, more fetid gas,
thick as London fog, sewer smells.

Ramon was translucent, fluorescent
with duodenal slime. This Honduras

is some kind of country. I am
purified. Reborn. I am somehow woman.

The Don was feeling mythical: Jonah,
Ahab, Pinochio's papa, Thor Heyerdahl.

Pedro was wishing they'd listened
to the Colonel. He was yanked from his

wet doldrums by the Don, who seemed
to be saying in gargle-form, Kill Ramon.

Pedro slipped a gall stone 'round Ramon,
and the thin man sank with all

the other lukewarm souls, only to bob
and bubble over in lipids of lava.

But then, praise God and/or providence,
he got sucked up in a borscht storm,

a sudden chasm of earthquake proportions,
flung backwards, the way Abrogast

went down the stairs in *Psycho*,
torque-speed, toward the sphincter.

The Don and Pedro went down a sea
of yellow brine and limited consciousness

until they were expelled
in a bubbling puddle. They spelunked

their way to safety again.
The Don was purposive, full of

philosophic telos. That never happened.
It was the work of the moorish magician.

Pedro knew it did happen, sure as the
leadpipe cinch on Orion's belt it did.

Oft, people tell jokes after near-death
experience. And so the Don waxed jovial.

What's a candle got in common with two
men from Helsinki? Pair a Finns.

Ramon got it. He roared, resurrected
as he was, brown polyps of pockmarked skin.

Muy chistoso, he said. I survived,
hoisted by the farce of a full petard,

I survived. Hosannah. Kill Ramon,
the Don whispered, and Pedro drove a stake

through the thin man's heart. Blood
came out like cottage cheese. They crossed

themselves and started off, filled with
a mix of melancholy-mirth. They realized

the rafts that saved them
were the mules who formerly bore them.

When they had gained their silhouettes,
two brown sun spots on the horizon line,

Ramon arose and sharded the stake.
Stigmata grew where the splintered wood

had been. He flexed his arms
and followed them. No trouble keeping up.

8.

Musing over the morning meal—filet
of armadillo, stale pulque and a wet

gazpacho strudel of beans, Pedro
was given to questions, the list of which

follows: Why was I born?
Why am I here? Why are we here,

nation-wise? I never asked in Vietnam,
so now I'm asking. They don't want us,

they don't like us. I saw *The Godfather,*
all parts, ten times. Is there perchance

a bigger mafia than we can imagine?
Why do we put the severed heads

of dead presidents on one side of coins,
extinct animals on the other?

Why are epics all about men, with women
serving only as sirens, saloon girls,

things that go boomp in the night,
and never as pals, long-suffering friends,

saddle companions? I miss Spot.
Why do I miss my mule? Why do the words

Jesus jenny come up when I think of her,
who gave her immovable hips and gristle

to save my hide? What is pride?
A rhyme? A festoon? A pecadillo?

Who killed Cock Robin? I really must know.
And why did Winnie Pooster call himself

Mr. Sanders? Makes me think of the Colonel,
who went poof-sfumato like laundry steam.

And why can't I kill Ramon? Silver bullets,
stake through the heart, gall stone,

something spooky-religious. He has migraines,
wood angina, he says stupid things,

is full of *pesadumbre,* but he won't
go down. He looks good to me.

I want to share my knapsack with him,
do a pedicure, go down Space Mountain.

And why is my Don, like all patriarchs,
so easy to obey and hard to love?

And who is Sid that we can't find him
hiding behind every rock? What kind

of name is Sid? We might as well call
him Siddharta. Or Sisyphus. And why

does the Don get all the proverbs?
I got proverbs. *Lo que dices me distrae*

de lo que eres. Rage is to age
what truth is to youth. Gloom and doom

from womb to tomb. You always love
the one you hurt. I got me proverbs plenty.

Nobody answered him. Nobody paid him
any heed. The Don, blistered with pulque,

slept through the morning, dreaming
lucid flying dreams of Dulcie. He was a

mockingbird, and Dulcie's snow-white thighs
were birch trees in which to land.

Ramon, who could not dream, but could
easily espy on the dreams of others,

abated himself under his serape.

9.

Along the road they met the wayward,
the windblown, hobos, hippies, highwaymen.

They met a doddering Englishman,
who addressed the Don in very bad Spanish:

El medico Vivapiedra, yo presumo?
The Don eschewed all translation,

fought fire with fire, question
with question, pre-socratic to the core,

and spoke the universal tongue of myth:
Do you know Sid Hammett? I say,

said Stan, for that was his name,
I've read a bit of his brother Dashiell.

There are so many sotting Jesuits about
you weary of Chesterton, Graham Greene.

The utterly bold try Malcolm Lowry,
but I'm a bit of a bludgeon for crime,

hairy-faced nasties, that sort of thing.
I'd give my right teat for a page of Dick Francis,

but oh posh and bother. I say,
spot of tea for a weary traveler?

That he named both mules
in the space of one question

enraged the Don. Kill him, he said.
No más, said Ramon. Kill Ramon too.

Pedro slew Stan with an architect's crossbow,
for even his weapons had regressed in time,

and then slew Ramon, who waited the dart
in the manner that frescoes depict Saint Sebastian.

Ramon lay low the allotted time, then arose
and pulled the arrow out of his eye.

Great, he said. I'm blind in one eye.
You can see out the other

was the ethereal response.
Mother cojones, Ramon complained.

This turning the other chica gets
a little stale. Tad trite. Hackneyed.

To wit: I'm tired of being killed.
You say the Don will repent his ways.

He has no ways. He's an automaton.
Kill Ramon. That's all he says.

And Mister Peter Towers in Spanish drag,
he's way cool when he looks at me.

I don't know which to fear more,
being killed in front or mounted from behind.

He wants to piggyback me, that's for sure.
And now I have only one good eye

to watch him with. Okay, so ending a plaint
with a preposition is less than divine.

So, sue me. Souls, I'd walk over hot coals
for. You know that. But sexual confusion

is another story. And the old man
has such innocent erotic dreams

he's got me baiting my hook. Yes,
I remember Onan, but you don't remember

what it's like to be in a body.
They got a saying: Use it or lose it.

The Eighties were the Me generation.
The Nineties are supposed to be I-Thou,

but I'm the only one who knows it.
It's a curse to see that far ahead.

What's that you say? With only one eye
I can stay in the now. Hey, *gracias,*

I really appreciate that O.T. sense
of humor. Up thine. And what's with

making those two stinking mules
martyr-saints? I rot down here,

while those scabby burros wander
the *campos eliseos* in search of cud

and sacred cowchips. And don't send
that wheezebag sycophant Assisi Francis

to sermon me on the birds that don't gather,
lilies of the field and toil,

I'm too busy. I've got my gringo friends
to goatherd. Sorry about the non-burial,

Stan. *Soit.* Thus saying, he gave off
speech, the heavens closed, and heavy rain

commenced to fall. Ramon knew full well
this wasn't the end of the Western world,

that much had been promised long ago.
This was a personal pour, a mild rebuff,

better than leeches, boils or locusts,
so he bit his tongue and kept on walking.

10.

They left Honduras with heavy hearts
on the backs of three borrowed camels,

all with udders: theatrical milkers,
called dromedaries, left to graze,

riderless, in Easter grass. They
responded to the names Frank, Incense

and Myrtle, but the Don would have none
of that. I shall call mine Traveler.

You can call yours Spot. He and Pedro
waited for Ramon to baptize his beast.

Ramon felt a certain maji displacement
the others couldn't comprehend.

He wanted to call his camel Man,
for the beast that makes promises,

or Ship of the Desert, Humpty Dumpty,
Iscariot, other standard-bearing

names, but he settled on Ahmal,
which is French for Too Bad. The Don

spoke in an old Western twang,
as though he were heading a posse,

Okay, boys, let's ride. They all
put spurs to the flanks of their mounts

and inched their way into Salvador.

11.

El Salvador was musk and smoke,
sturm und drang, fire and ice,

the world at war, every which way.
Colonel Trump was waiting for them.

You boys made primavera time
and fresh ponies to boot. I got a new

Apache here, take you back to old
El Paso, hero's welcome, ten-gun salute,

tour of White Sands, available
women, all walks of life. Let's

just say the eagle has landed.
But they would not. So the Colonel

demurred and let them pass. Ramon
protested, I'd walk a mile for a . . .

he was going to say *cerveza,*
but the Colonel interrupted:

You already got one. Skip the mile.
Go the whole nine yards instead.

They passed the guffaws of FMLN,
the snooty insouciance of government troops,

and entered a kingdom of potpourri
where they met with the following:

Liz Taylor, Norman Mailer,
the Ancient Mariner, Bob Marley and a Wailer.

Joe DiMaggio, Caravaggio,
a Mozart andante and adagio.

Cleavon Little, E. Power Biggs,
Y.A. Tittle and Bobby Riggs.

Ronald Reagan, Menachem Begin,
Carl Sagan, Dickens' Fagin.

Ram Dass, Cantinflas, Tom
Thumb, Tweedledum, Octavio Paz.

Jane Eyre, perne in a gyre,
the Mormon Tabernacle Choir,

and all of them singing, *sotto voce*,
We didn't start the fire.

They met three damsels in distress,
all in torn and tattered dress,

bruise marks, blood clots,
ousted by the Huguenots

for bad hygiene. Miladies,
the Don said, it wounds me

to the quick to see you so
disposed. In olden days knights

errant might have jousted
for your troth. I give these rings

from all ten fingers
and all the money in my pouch.

God bless your maidenheads.
The women cackled like hags

and left with the money bags.
Pedro could not stoop to conquer,

so he protested to his boss.
Them's *putas,* Don, common whores,

not damsels in distress.
The Don countered. Are they

any less distressed for all
their life's experience? Listen . . .

Pedro waited. To what?
To silence, the Don proclaimed.

Listen is an anagram for silent.
And here's another: in the garden of Eden

the respent serpent repents the present.
Pedro couldn't argue there.

Ramon looked skyward for succor.
His reply came down as heavy rain.

Farther down the road a piece,
three more damsels in distress,

but these were microscopic maids,
the size of fruit flies. Ye be

a dog, one of them tweeted. Pedro
declined to intervene. They might be

fleas, looking for a dog to roost,
but one thing's sure: them's

Liliputas, *mi patron.* Don't be swayed.
Hush, my trusty manservant, don't

be rude in the company of women.
They speak not of 'dogs,' but of 'gods,'

for they are the sometimes dyslexic.
Are ye indeed 'strat,' wee one?

She nodded no, which meant yes.
And what are thy 'seman'? 'Gem.'

Ah 'Gem,' to be sure. 'Yma' and 'Oj.'
Enchanté. I dare not ask

what befell thy sistern. I have
no 'yenom' to give thee, 'sala,' but

I will give thee the 'dlog' filling
from my 'dipsuc.' Ouch. There 'tis.

What's that ye say? 'Dial'?
He whispered something like No Mark Us,

and he and Pedro went on their way,
while the Liliputas waylaid Ramon.

A lesson to you, Pedro, the Don said.
What Thanatos cannot accomplish

Eros can. A silk purse. A sow's ear.
Let's not be caught pound-foolish.

Pedro couldn't argue there.
A watched boil never pops,

he would be the first to admit,
so they rode off in search of Sid.

When Ramon caught up with them,
bestride Ahmal, he was still jumping.

Fidget, shimmy, bounce and twitter,
he did them all. The others watched.

He's got a Walkman, Pedro thought.
Why do you undulate? the Don asked.

Déjà vu, I guess. His face
was flushed and all forsworn.

I never thought it could be like that.
I still don't, Pedro thought.

Foiled again, the Don looked up.
Heavy rain was his reply.

12.

In El Salvador every green thing
moved and smelled like sulphur.

Every brown thing died and stayed
unburied. Bullets traced the air

like flushed quail, with no apparent
aim or target. Ratatattat,

and then retort. The silence
between was louder than guns.

They chanced upon Erasmo, a Jesuit
in dreadlocks, Jamaica-brown,

a lilting, Rasta rhetoric,
an AK47 in one hand, a basket

of fruit in the other.
He brayed, he grinned, he shuffled,

never stood on both feet at once
and did his stand-up monologue.

We hear you be coming, mahn,
to our little war-torn corner

of the world. The news,
she come from far and wide.

Far don't say too much at all,
but wide, he talk a little bit.

He say you come on burros, mahn,
but here you are on camels,

just like kings. No problem.
Bienvenidos todos. He bowed low.

He had Tracy Chapman hair,
Sammy Davis eyes. Like your frock,

Don. Your blade, knickers, boots
and spurs. *Très élan.* Like, mahn,

coals to Leeds, tires to anachronism.
My fifteen minutes to be famous,

don't stop me now. It's the blood
of the feud down here, a rancid

bad time for Jesuits, payback
for inquisitions, the rack

and wheel of fortune. Like Yellowman
say, Under me fat thing, the big bamboo

of third-world countries, who's
on first and second, the Pope,

the Papa Doc of doctrine, and all
his semi-intentional phallus Sees.

No, mahn, I don't know no semite
shaman name a Sid. We got *Santoria,*

mahn, what do we need of Sid?
Pigs' feet, chicken heads, survival

of the pagan gods. We put
the cat back in catechism,

and it's a black cat. I can tell
you this and then no more.

My apocalypse are sealed.
Hey, Pedrocito, don't try no tricks.

You cannot pull on me.
I pull on you first. You see

my guns and roses, eh? The gun
is a fake, she fires blanks,

but my roses cover up my eggs,
huevos, what you call them,

hand grenades. So now the Don,
he wants my benediction? Okay.

A clever ploy. I drop my gun,
but not my eggs. Go in pieces.

A pox vobiscum. Dieu vous blesse.
A hard man is good to find.

Sid, come out, wherever you are.
Give these three gulags a call,

a high five, burning bush, any ole
sign at all, if design govern

in a thing so small. He wished
them reggae sunsplash and was gone.

The Don broke the silence.
Kill Ramon. Pedro gagged Ramon

with one of Erasmo's hand grenades,
tickled Ramon, forced him to swallow,

then showed him the pulled pin.
Ramon looked up, and the ensuing rain

blunted the explosion. He left
entrails along the ground,

but he stayed seated
astride Ahmal, who lost his hump.

13.

They stopped by a pond
where a nude girl swam.

She was spritely and gossamer
as panty hose. Their tongues

wagged, like lamb dogs to whistles.
The scene was bucolic, well

past oral. She said her name
was Eco, and with a look

of recognition, the Don mistook
her for an Italian semiotician.

Ever the cavalier, he tried
to address her in limited French.

Honi soit qui mal y pense.
I see London, I see France.

Rome wasn't built in a day.
Florence Nightingale. *Uno,*

Padua. Trieste. *Quattrocento.*
Verdi, *que te quiero* Verdi.

Veni, vidi, da Vinci.
Respeto a tu padre, Michelangelo.

Amo, amas, amat.
There is some s . . . I will not eat.

She didn't understand Italian,
but she repeated every word.

Do you know a man named Sid?
Do you know a man named Sid?

Of course I do, or I wouldn't be asking.
Of course I do . . . it fell to Pedro

to explain. She's not that kind
of Eco, boss. She's Pete and

repeat, like a parakeet,
a mockingbird, a myna bird.

She's got no parley of her own.
Tautology, redundancy, you're

going to hear what you want to hear,
but it's all the same to her.

She reverbs. That's all she does.
Capish? Eco nodded, clapping hands,

as though to say, By Jove, you've got it,
if only someone said it first.

I see, said the Don. By Jove.
She plays charades with words.

Ramon pointed to the Don's skull,
as though to explain the Don to her.

There's a rattan chair in there,
in which nobody sits. *Tabula rasa.*

La Raza, she repeated, giving him
the power first. *Reggaza* strip,

the Don thought, semitically,
still stuck on Sid, like a lug nut

on a radial tire. A certain Sadean
cruelty betook poor Pedro. There was

mileage to be made of doublespeak.
Putative. See men. Va Va Gina

Lollabrigida. Mike Hunt. Was
Clare Booth Luce? Spermatozoa.

Go Nadia Comaneci. Pissenlit.
Heinous. It's Meg, Ma.

Ramon read his mind and cringed
like kindling in Vermont *après*-ski.

Getting the girl to talk dirty
by way of puns and homonyms

that she must perforce repeat
seemed the worst sort of coprolalia,

beneath the pure pursuits
of chivalry, which were necessarily

chaste, as villains by Keystone Cops.
Chaste and chasten, the roots

of purity in punishment,
which brought him sadly back to Sade.

Echo could almost hear their thoughts,
and her lips were beseeched

with half-formed words in three
directions. There was nothing worse

than having to speak first
the hand-held thoughts of silent men,

the curse of women everywhere.
But she forgave them, as women will,

this gender flaw in men. She was raw,
her soggy skin was waterlogged,

her breasts like buoys at the Alamo,
they wouldn't come in, she couldn't

get out, the eerie way that water
comes between men and women,

and so she pointed to the man
who had mocked her, spurned her love,

broken her heart, incurred her wrath,
the beautiful boy by the edge of the pond.

They followed her finger, forgot
her completely. The beautiful boy

by the edge of the pond saw them
coming, reflections in water,

at which he fixed his stare,
but never looked up. He nodded,

but he never looked up. The fact
that he never looked up allowed them

to speak about him in the third
person singular, as though he were

absent. The lad has dashing
good looks, said the Don. 'T'is true,

said Pedro, and yet he don't look
so good. Look at the way

his chin digs his chest.
He's been looking down so long

he wouldn't know up from supper.
Maybe he's obsessed, said Ramon.

There's something to be said for
concentration in these scattered times.

Let's query him, said the Don.
What's your name, sonny boy?

Narciseo, *señor*. That ain't
a very manly name, but okay.

Have you seen a gent named Sid,
moorish spots and mighty picaresque

in a stay-home kind of way?
You know the dude? No, señor,

I've seen no one but myself
for the longest time. You see,

I'm stuck on myself, my image at least.
Well sir, the Don said, proverb in hand,

Reflections should oughta reflect a bit
before sending back images. Besides,

you ain't that cute, know what I mean?
Narciseo sighed, then took up speech

like a poor man his ploughshare. I wasn't
always thus, señor. I used to love

the otherness of others. I didn't mind
the master-slave, that dot matrix

of all human relations, I revelled
in alterity. Sartre was wrong.

Hell is looking in the mirror
and never looking anywhere else.

I wanted to kiss the girls
and tell, just like any other boy.

I took this German
au pair named Lotte

to the edge of this pond.
She looked back and was turned into salt.

Dogs have lapped it up over time.
You're stepping in what's left of her.

She was the lucky one. I didn't
look back, and what did I get?

The one in the water, skinny-dipping,
she comes on to me, mimics me

my every move, repeats my every word,
like Simon says, minus Simon.

Well, I had a double dose
of bad luck and broken heart,

so I said, *No más, gracias.*
But the banshee put a curse on me.

If she couldn't have me, nobody could.
Made me fall in love with myself.

So, stuck I am. I can't do squat.
She bobs and plops, dog-paddles

all day long. I can hear her,
making sport of me. It's the revenge

of ears on the eyes, repression
of the scopic drive, female echo

over the male gaze. Doesn't that
frost you, strike a sympathetic chord,

you being male and all? They
were moved. Even the camels

were moved to tears, especially
the humpless eunuch Ahmal,

and camels don't shed tears
or anything liquid lightly.

What must we do? the Don inquired.
Do what you must, the pretty boy said.

Okay, then. Being of sound mind
and body, I hereby order you, Pedro,

to put this Narsissy boy
out of his misery. Shoot the blighter,

put out his eyes, gut him where
he stands. Pedro's weapons had so

regressed that he was hard-pressed
to perform a quick homicide.

But he found a stone, made a sling
and slew the pretty boy post-haste.

Shouldn't we bury him? Naw,
said the Don, dogs gotta eat.

Well, shouldn't I be killing Ramon?
Naw, said the Don, why try?

The demise of Narciseo just then
caused a very curious thing:

suddenly, Echo had eyes for Ramon.
The Don was ecstatic. I hope

you can swim, Ray. You gotta give in
to the little goddess or be seeing

your sorry self for all eternity.
Either way, you're stuck.

We'll leave Ahmal, just in case.
Vámonos, Pedro, before she changes

her mind. Pedro was reminded
of a proverb from Baudelaire,

The Bad Flowers: Hurry up, before
the second glance comes to spoil everything.

It took two days, but it wasn't long
before Ramon caught up with them.

He had even pistol-whipped
Ahmal to a canter. How, pray tell,

the Don chewed his words,
did you escape the aquatic Medusa?

I refused her advances, Ramon said.
It was eerie. Don't talk about

Great Lakes, Pedro said. It was
just a pond. Get on with it.

Okay, okay. So I refused. So then
she put the curse on me. It was

neat, exceedingly neat, at first.
I never thought I was handsome before,

but damn if I didn't have
fetching good looks. Just me

and my pool-peignoir. All day
to do my toilette. I memorized

my gums. Counted gray hairs.
It was better than tantric yoga.

Pedro couldn't contain himself:
HOW DID YOU ESCAPE? he screamed.

I summoned all my will, every
last ounce of resolve, raised my chin,

looked up to heaven, and sure enough,
a heavy rain commenced to fall,

heavy enough to piddle out
my simulacrum. I was twenty-three

skidoo. Ahmal didn't want to go.
His reflection in the pool

had his hump back, which he liked,
prosthesis in the pond, which he liked,

but I said, Sahara, and beat him
with my fetish stick, and *voilà,*

here we are, the three amigos,
reunited. I thought Honduras

was a hunker-down funky kind
of country. But El Salvador

can hold its own for bungle
in the jungle. And I was thinking

how thirteen is such a bad-rap
unlucky kind of number,

but, if you let it go on long enough,
give it play, let it sway,

it's prime like one or seven
eleven. And then I was thinking . . .

The Don had already tuned him out.
We should have prayed for drought,

he thought, at a loss for proverbs.
Pedro too was lost in thought.

I'd like to piggyback Ramon.
Maybe that would shut him up.

14.

Death squads run rough-shod
over Latino America, every other

country, like a horror game
of hopscotch, rayuela-riots,

women without teeth, bleeding
from the bowels, men with stubble,

moronic grins, drugged and leaning
on bayonettes, by accident,

and everywhere the gringo touch,
visible, invisible, like lichen

on the ivy, peat on the moss,
wort on William, the mess in mestizo,

the ravished chancre on the sore.
A watched boil never pops,

they knew the proverb all too well,
and still they were ill-prepared

for all the plagues and pestilence:
frogs, boils, corns, bunions,

everything that afflicts the feet:
leeches, newts, efts, iguanas,

click beetles, dors and salvadors,
every green slimy creature

that riveted, burped, sucked blood,
carried malaria, disturbed the peace,

the land was gross with animal phlegm,
insect imagos, nit sacks, larval lard.

Footnote: the French Foreign Legion,
before they disbanded from syphilis

and *mal du siècle,* tested its members
for possible spies by making them say

the one word for frog: *grenouille.*
Impossible for a non-native speaker.

That's how they caught Mata Hari.
Every language has just such a word

to catch spies. In English, *medicinal.*
In Spanish, it's *ferrocarril.*

The double trill cannot be done
by a non-native speaker. So when the Don

summed up the situation in Salvador
by using the passive periphrastic,

Christiani delendi sunt, the others
were not surprised. It was right and just.

15.

And then one night it happened.

In the mirth of piebald mountains,
the musky darkness like an athlete's towel,

the moon playing Scrabble with the clouds,
the camels off grazing on parched jackstraw,

the Don obscured in sweet dreams of Dulcie,
it happened, oh my best beloved.

Pedro piggybacked Ramon.

The plaintive cry of wild coyotes
disturbed the birds in the live oak trees.

Otherwise, the night was theirs.
In the morning, they made spoons.

Ramon snuggled up and said,
A peso for your thoughts.

I was thinking on war and intimacy,
how sex feels good after massacres,

how after a siege we sang the old songs,
And the Khe Sanhs go rolling along . . .

Yes, I know, Petey, but what about me?
Well, 'Mon, you sure live up to your name.

If dinosaurs were buried here, they'd
be up and Adam, know what I mean?

The Don's got a proverb: the wise man
don't enter the front door without first

knowing where the back door is.
And vice verses, know what I mean?

But if the Don says to kill you,
I must comply. No hard feelings?

Ramon responded with a proverb:
au contraire, mon frère, the whole nine yards.

16.

Costa Rica, resplendent like a jewel,
green as a theme park, arroyos

everywhere, Ireland and El Dorado,
a Toys 'R' Us for botanists.

Ferns fat as nerf balls and overhung
grapes, purple as the sage

Parmenides, who interdicted them
as the no thing not to think about.

Pedro popped a couple purple seedless.
Grapes, I mean grapes, are the popcorn of fruit.

Colonel Trump was waiting for them,
leaning on an invisible Stealth,

defying gravity. *Carpe diem,* the Don
warned. We killed him too, Pedro said.

You boys are wanted for murder
in six different countries, Trump said.

Interpol is interested. Castro laughs
at us. Where were you when the Bay

of Puercos went down, like a bad case
of tricky gnossis? Mad Max a Million

caused less stir. We're down here
stirring foment and you show up.

You're messing up our coup attempts.
They passed on without reply, as though

he too were stealth, infected with
invisibility. They met up with the

drug cartel: Ochoa, Gacha, Escobar,
a caravan of pink Lincolns.

We're lost. We're looking for Panama.
Ramon pointed south. They went thataway.

They met Frank Nitti. The Don was aghast.
You're the ghost of Christmas Past,

he said. No way, Frank said. WP.
WordPerfect? No, Witness Protection.

How's my Shy-Town? Windy. Still
Aeolian, huh? And the Bears and Cubs?

Still in hibernation. Good one, Don.
And that Loch Ness monster, what became of him?

He worked for Public Health during the war.
Fought the spread of venereal disease,

died a pauper in Pennsylvania. You
don't say, Don. He fought what Al got,

ha ha. Them two was always twined.
Cain and Abel. Siskel and Ebert,

Heloise and Abelard. Give my best
to the syndicate. I loved them boys.

Say, Frank, you ever see a man named Sid?
I don't use proper names down here,

Don. Everything's señor. Besides,
I wouldn't remember anyway. I won't

remember you tomorrow. I got a disease
called Al's Hammers, I guess, from being

Capone's peen all those years. I'll
say to you what I yelled at the Pope

in his bubble-top. *Vaya con diablo*,
Juan Pablo. Ha ha. That's a good one,

Frank. Sincerely. Then he sauntered off,
shoeless, like a fisherman. The next day,

they met Ambrose Bierce, he of the short
short stories, looking like Peyton Farquhar,

ring around the collar. I'm holding on
and hiding out, he said, for a duel

with Old Ironsides, himself. Ray Burr.
No earthly good can come of a Burr.

You're a writer, Ambro, the Don said,
using the familiar. Have you seen

a scribe named Sid? Bierce paused.
Olive complexion, leaning toward the semite

side, verbose, can't write a lick,
jaws all day about Hemingway,

the American macho beer-swilling
impotent narcissist, the importance

of being Ernest, hated like hell
that he fished with Fidel, that one?

Yes, that one. No. Haven't seen him,
but I'll tell him, iffen I do,

you're here to call him out. In the
meantime, knights errant, beware

of sodbusters, wooly sheep people,
men named Roberto what call themselves Bob,

Knights Templar and Knights in White Satin.
Thankee, Bierce, for this advice,

and might I whisper same to you?
This carnal lud is Pedro, he's part of my posse,

but this varmint is called Ramon.
For all we know, he might be the Burr

you're looking for. Much obliged, Don,
I'll call him out. You do that,

Ambro, but please to wait until me
and Pedro have safely passed. Sure thing,

Don, but don't he need a second? Naw,
he's had plenty of time. They mounted up

and left Ramon, standing back-to-back
with Ambrose Bierce. As they started

stepping forty paces, pistols cocked,
Ramon was heard to say, I liked

"Chickamauga," its sparse incredulity,
the diffidence of identical twins

opposed at war. To which the author
made reply, Keep walking, Ray.

The Don was ebullient, craw
full of proverbs. These he spewed:

Frontier justice is mighty swift
and twice as gullible.

And: many are galled,
but feuds are chosen.

17.

They stopped at a cantina to drink
pulque, sit a spell, watch some telly.

Two men named Sacco and Vanzetti
were hosting a show called *Al Cine*,

film clips with simulcast comments
in six different tongues, a slight

time lag between the sound and the
moving lips: skatty, like jazz.

Sacco, *tu m'emmerdes avec Alea* . . .
Memories of Underdevelopment . . .

semper ubi sub ubi. . . totemo oishii desu . . .
the lack of flashbacks in leftist films . . .

Bōm dacado, Vanzetti, *mon vieux cochon,*
nicht verstehen . . . poder a la gente.

Señores y señoras, hasta entonces
las sillas en el balcon están cerradas.

Blistered anew with pulque, the Don
began his dream deferred of Dulcie.

Say Don, Pedro said, himself in no pain,
how long we going to stay after Sid?

We'll ride these camels to Camelot.
In truth, poor Traveler and Spot

were well-nigh ridden out,
tongues hung low like Tiresias' dugs

in a wasteland where the only query
was, Do I dare to eat a peach?

The only Round Table they could espy
was the yoke of an ox at a trough nearby.

But then the familiar wheeze of Ahmal
lifted their spirits. Ramon clambered down

like a bow-legged Dutchman who'd listed
on one ship too many to put *pied à terre.*

I'm back, he hiccoughed. Pour me a brew.
Pedro made up for the Don's cool demeanor

by hugging Ramon. You're quite a man, Ray.
Don't call me a Surrealist. Bring me

the head of Alfredo Garcia. I'm famished.
First, tell us how you survived. Perils

of Pauline, boys, I thought I was a goner.
Bierce was fierce, a first-rate shootist.

He shot first, shot fastest, kept on shooting.
But lo and behold, I was still standing.

He hit my harmonica every which way
but loose, I guess. Key of E flat's

all I got left. I let him think I was
Saint George or something. He waited

for me to pull on him, but I just told him
to go write an epic. I figured that

was spanking enough for a short story
writer. I done made the world safe for Burrs.

Wild Bill Hiccup, Pedro said,
fresh from his shoot at the Hoquet Corral.

18.

The lives of knights errant
are not always full. There are lulls

in the action, when trysting
and jousting cease and desist.

They found themselves drydocked
with their ships of the desert,

at calm, as it were, oasis of stasis.
Nothing to do in their rented room

in beautiful downtown La Quinta
but eat out at Denny's: brontosaurus

burguesas, asea in a gripping
salsa picante. The Don said,

I see a windmill outside my window.
That's a satellite dish, Pedro replied,

two hundred eighty channels.
We can even get the Falklands.

Ramon was toggling the remote:
the San Francisco baseball Giants,

the New York football Giants.
Call it what you will, said the Don,

they might be giants, but me, I
still see a windmill outside my window.

They played Chivalry Pursuit.
Pedro asked the questions.

In the "Art" category: name
the prevailing aesthetic at Camelot.

Ramon buzzed first. Art deco.
Nokay. Art decalogue. Wrong. Don?

Arthur for Arthur's sake. Kee-rect,
give that man a beer. In the category

"Sexes and Hexes," what was wrong
with King Arthur's marriage? Once again,

Ramon buzzed first. He was gone a lot.
That is incorrect. Don? He could

pierce evil, but he couldn't lance a lot.
Correct. And now in the gangster category. . .

Unfair, Ramon said. There weren't
any gangsters in chivalry. Don?

Would you care to respond? I would.
Was Hegel unfair to Schlegel? Pamela

to Shamela? Juliet Mitchell to
Jacqueline Rose? Lacan to Kant?

I stand corrected, Ramon said.
Let play continue, unnotice me.

Who was head honcho in *Romance of the Rose*?
No buzz, Ramon? Discretion is the better part

of velour. To you, Don. Uh, I have to
use the little boy's room. Ramon

became suspicious. He's been gone too long.
I hear no flush. He's in there cheating.

Quiet flows the Don, Pedro said. The Don
returned with new resolve, ready to

target his market and market his target.
Charley Magnum, he said correctly.

We're about to enter the bonus round.
Values are doubled. Good luck to you both.

In the category "Lit. and Lit./Crit."
what kind of potion did Tristan imbibe?

A shandy. That's correct, Don. Please
remember to buzz before speaking.

The Don put his epaulettes in the pot.
Okay, Ramon. The Don has upped his ante.

Now up yours. Ramon gave his green
good-luck scapular. Can I name

the next category? You have no score,
Ramon, so the point is moot, but I don't see

why not. Okay, then. "Oh Heavenly Deities."
How many angels on the head of a pin?

Sorry, Ramon. You buzzed too quickly.
Don? Ten, if they're erose.

Archangels, three. Wing span, you know.
That's right, boss. I quit, said Ramon,

beginning to sulk like a polio vaccine.
I still see a windmill outside my window.

He's batty, Ramon said to Pedro.
They went to a square dance in downtown

La Quinta. They listened to the auctioneer.
Aleman left with your partner,

and all the Germans went izquierda.
Shoot the star, and they all shot the sheriff,

but they did not shoot the deputy.
The Don stood next to a bandaged man

named King Tut-in-Common. Myself,
I wait for the bunny-hop, Tut said,

fanning himself. Cozy fan, Tut.
I've heard that before, the bandaged king said.

He looked like Jimmy Cagney
in *Public Enemy*. Enemy, enema,

one word led to another, and
pretty soon the Don was asking:

How do you null and void there, Tutter?
How do you defecate? He answered

in a clipped British accent: (aside:
why do all foreigners speak English

in a clipped British accent? Or,
perversely, why do all Americans abroad

sound like they stepped off the stagecoach
in *High Noon*?) Interesting party conversation,

Don, but I don't mind telling you.
I get backed up from time to time.

In those compelling instances,
I go to see my cairo-practor.

Her name is Mia Pharaoh.
She's very good with her digits.

Pedro was making small talk too,
with Sahib, King Tut's attendant.

I'm a nomad. Pedro nodded, congenially.
I'ma no mad at you, neither.

You speak very bad English, Sahib said.
Where were you born? East L. A.

It's west of the world. Ramon, for his part,
was making advances on a veiled maid

of King Tut's entourage. Her name was
Marena, but Ramon thought

that the M was silent. In my language,
he said, 'Arena' means *sand.*

In my language, she responded,
'Marena' means *water.* It means the Nile,

but we cannot pronounce this word back home,
its overuse having been annihilated.

I'm wondering what's behind that veil.
Can I take a little peek? No, *señor,*

what is hidden is forbidden,
a no-no, taboo-boo. Besides,

you were the one who shot the Sharif.
Yes, funny girl, but I did not shoot

the deputy. You don't like Westerners?
Little and less. To the west

we are besieged by Saharikrishnas,
looking for airports. To the east

we are besieged by Dayanetics
and Ziontology. It's hopeless,

like kibbee without pine nuts.
I'd like to father your child, Arena.

Another taboo-boo. Besides,
they have tied my Ethiopian tubes

with an accordion knot. The princess
sleeps without the pea, the oyster

has been cloistered on the half-shell,
Cleopatra's mattress has asparagus,

my clock has no wake-up call,
the pit has left my pendulum,

the purr in my loins has been purloined.
You might as well call me Clytemnestra.

Nay, Clytie, you'll no wallflower or
sunflower be. 'Arena' means *sand,*

so I'll call thee Cassandra.
Enough of mything persons, she lisped.

My throat for you is a veiled hollow
that can a whole condominium swallow.

They left the Great Hall for the parking lot.
Midsummer's Night. Traveler was humping Spot,

while Ahmal foraged for cowchips.
Marena was ready to percale Ramon.

Her veil revealed a vibrant bravura.
He undid her bra, but left her vura

intact. She was stacked. Loose lips
sink ships, but not when they're covered

with satin. She was skin, he was bone.
He was Punch, she was Judith. She was

Lolly, he was Pop. He was thrust,
she was parry. She was Hero,

he was oleander. He was Samson,
she was Delilacs. She was Lassie,

he was collieflour. He was cuckoo,
she was Fran, and, by default, Ahmal

was Ollie Ollie Exxon Free. Suffice
to say, they were lots of people,

but she gloved him like a fit.
She whined the spectrum of the vowels:

a-e-i-o-u. He panted, My name
is not Housemans, and you owe me nothing.

But he was clearly disemvowelled.
Meanwhile, inside the Great Hall,

Sahib pontificated Pedro. I speak
the Pope's English, infallibly proper,

and I say to you, Let's go get lain.
You slay me, Sahib. Speaking of proverbs,

you're like the proverbial papal bull
in a china shop. All fiats. Nay,

said Sahib, I drive a Volvo. And I am
not Cathay's clown nor anything Ori-yentl.

Now let's go get lain.
I know a tar bar not far from here.

But how can we leave our bosses uncovered?
In my case, at least, there is no problem.

Look at them. The Godfather and mummy.
The family romance. Let's leave them

to explore the dark continence.
Okay, Sahib, but dwell on this:

a down lineman and a down pillow
are not the same: one is hard,

the other soft, yet both are down.
This is strange indeed, said Sahib.

In my language there is only one word
that can be hard and soft: the pita.

We shall learn more of each other's tongues
as we go to get lain in downtown La Quinta.

They left the Great Hall for the parking lot.
Midsummer's Night. Spot was humping Traveler,

while Ahmal foraged for cowchips.
Back in the Great Hall they were doing a Lindy.

You wait a long time for a bunny hop,
King Tut said. Sing me the songs of your youth.

A poem I wrote in the second grade.
Will that do? I wrote it in quatrains,

but here I must give it in couplets.
'My wife was the unfaithful Elizabeth,

I resolved, alas, to put her to death.
I deceived her into descending the stair.

She entered the cellar room.
She squirmed at last, I bound her fast,

My heart thumped with joy at her doom.
I lit the match and set her ablaze.

Oh how she started to scream.
She bobbed about to stamp it out.

I poured on some kerosene.
Ashes to ashes, dust to dust,

she curled up like pizza crust.
And when I doused her with turpentine,

I knew that she was finally mine.'
It's just a fragment, simply a shard

of a longer work. I was slightly
influenced at the time by Edgar Allan Poe.

Quoth the raven. Ligeia's tomb.
Usherfall and ulalume. Things like that.

Don't be so modest, King Tut said.
I, myself, went through a phase

of Solomon's songs, Kahlil Gibran,
not unlike your Rod McKuen, and Omar,

the tentmaker, he spoke to my soul.
Say but the word, and my hole shall be sealed.

Have you read *Blood and Guts in High School*?
You should. Hester Prynne, her scarlet A,

Omar, bloody kotex, teenage trauma.
Talk about casting aspersions,

that lady really knows how to throw a rug.
But enough of this cerebral palsy-walsy,

the Don interrupted. My blood runs hot
for a bandaged boy. Tut hushed him

with a gauzed hand. Take me hence,
and I shall explain this circumstance.

They left the Great Hall for the parking lot.
Midsummer's Night. Traveler was grooming Spot,

Spot was grooming Traveler, and the
unbridled Ahmal was posting up a baobab tree.

It's Midsummer's Night, King Tut said,
the ripe time for a miracle.

He undid the pin atop the royal head
and gave to the Don a leader of gauze

and adhesive strip. Here. Hold this
and thy tongue if you can. Be amazed.

Tut proceeded to swivel, Sufi-unravel,
a whirling dervish. At last, the Don

held from his hand a whole sarcophagus
of stale bandages. Who stood before him

was not King Tut, but a naked girl,
quite hirsute, of course, and full

of coffin sores and such, but naked
nonetheless, and quite becoming in a

simian sort of way. As you can see,
I am woman. My name is Beatriz Kino,

and I was just a little girl,
learning to cook and sew and knit

at the court of the impish boy king
when it was decided that I should be wrapped

in lieu of Tut. Imagine my surprise.
All life's stages slowed to a crawl.

It took thousands of years
to go through puberty

in the pyramid. You look shocked.
I have to tell you it wasn't uncommon

for kinglets like Tut to coward out
at the last minute. Innocent girls

got sa'ran-wrapped in their stead.
It's a kind of cosmic joke,

if you're of the gender that's laughing.
Aren't you cold? the Don asked.

My nipples are a little chilly.
These breasts have been in a training bra

for centuries. This is the first
I've seen them full-pop. Not too shabby.

So, you see, dear Dante, your arousal
saw through gauze. I just had to show you.

Yes, but aren't you at risk of disintegration?
Quite. I hadn't thought of that.

But death would be a welcome change
from mummification. Besides which,

we do believe in reincarnation.
I'm due for greatness, don't you think?

What is it you want from me, Queen Bee?
Full penetration. In what way?

In a straightforward hetero way.
But I am betrothed to dear Dulcinea,

who's long ago and far away.
She bides her time in my penthouse apartment

on Lake Shore Drive. That's in Chicago.
Dante, dear Dante, I know this is sudden,

but I have disrobed at the risk of death.
I know what *cago* means in these parts,

so don't give me lady of the lake.
We're not talking long commitment.

I'll be urn-dust by morning. Give
a girl what she wants, before she takes

the big boatride in the ark. All
his arguments allayed, he did as he was bade.

He was Peter Pan. She was peanut brittle.
He was William Butler Yeats and Harold.

She was simply Maude. He was Kris
Kristofferson. She was Minnie Pearl.

He was a stitch in time.
She was Methusaleh.

He was Young Goodman Brown.
She was Old Mother Hubbard

He was in the bulrushes.
She was Grandmother Moses.

The list goes on. Meanwhile,
at the other end of the parking lot,

Marena spoke in polyglot.
Ramon thought she was babbling.

I know who you are, Marena said.
Of course you do. In the biblical sense,

he added. Do you think, she said,
the signs have escaped me?

The bullet scar upon your brow,
the scab of the stake near to your heart,

the stomach distended like a multiparous
mom, the telltale signs of a

swallowed bomb? I have as many
scars as you. What do you make of that?

You're into pain? No, Ramon,
don't be inane. I'm a spirit guide,

just like you. You dog the Don,
I shepherd Tut. Well, lapis lazuli,

so you're in the business?
She nodded yes. They settled in

to shop-talk. Say, doesn't it gall you
when mules get halos and we get zilch?

Yes, she agreed, in our *Lives of the Saints*,
over half are comprised of camels.

And, hey, does it rain when you
look up for guidance? No. In Egypt

it gets more arid. Extra dry.
Wow. Different strokes for different blokes.

And do you know an Arab sorcerer
named Sid Hammett? Of course. Who doesn't?

And do you, Ramonito, know a bunny-hop
dancer named Cyd Charisse?

Well, up the down staircase,
of course I do. Shall we kiss and not tell?

We have already kissed, and we are
forbidden to intervene. You know the rules.

Rules are meant to be broken, no?
A heavy rain commenced to fall.

Meanwhile, in a tar bar not far
from there, Sahib and Pedro were sodden drunk.

Sahib was nonetheless still obsessed
with semantics. In your King's English

the word 'flaccid' is not like acid,
but rather Flack Sid. The first c, you see,

is unlike his brother. But why
should a word that means something soft

be hard to pronounce? Answer me that.
It's like with Nixon, ole Tricky Dick,

Do you think he still knows where it's at?
Of course.He's got it down pat.

Pedro, Pedro, you're pulling my leg.
Frankly, my dear, I don't divvy a gam.

I don't want to carp or complain,
but I thought we were going to get

ourselves lain. Take the cyclops
out for a walk. Where are the whores?

I think they're not coming.
Pedro sat up, suddenly sober.

Maybe they're down at the docks
meeting ships. At this hour? No.

Maybe there's something amiss
with this bar? Like any other.

It's full of drunk tars, bad music,
desperation. It's like any other.

Then maybe it's a holy day,
and they're forbidden to wear their hawks.

Hawk their wares, I mean.
No, Pedro, it is no holy day.

It has to do with your friends,
I'm afraid. You see, at this moment

they're having sex. Both of them?
Yes. Together? Of course not.

Ramon is with the wild Marena,
whose real name is Maritrones.

Your master has mastered my master.
What? That twiggy little bandaged boy?

No boy. They say a nun is a buoy.
I thought all nuns were girls, Sahib.

How do you know? I have a nose
for pharaohmones. Even old ones.

No. How do you know they're having sex?
Well, it's ever been a curious thing,

since I can't see in the past or future,
but I have terrific peripheral vision.

But what's that got to do with us?
We are denied, that they be fulfilled.

How long have you known this?
It was always scripted so.

But you were the one who wanted
so much to get ourselves lain.

It was a ruse to get you aroused.
With you around, the Don and madonna

could never have clicked.
Actually, I'm quite asexual.

Elocution's my cup of tea.
Damn, Sahib, I gotta tell you,

you've been sipping the oolong too long.
If you didn't have a turban

on top of your head, your jets
would explode. How do you get off?

Oh, I deplane with all the rest.
Damn. The Don is getting his cookies

crumbled, and I'm left to look
like the Pillsbury Doughboy.

So, Ped. May I call you Ped?
Tell me about the Don's Dulcinea.

How do you know about her?
Lateral hearing. Sideways ears.

They're not so keen, north and south,
but east and west, I don't mean to brag,

but I can hear the entire equator.
So, what can you hear back at the dance?

Many moans. Slurpy sounds.
Like eating gruel without a spoon,

like cats lap up a plate.
Pantagruel meats Puss in Boots.

Yes, Ped. Now tell me about Dulcinea.
What's to tell? She's a farmer's daughter,

and all the jokes are true.
I forgot. You don't have farmers.

Anyway, she's from a farm,
a prosperous farm in Dixon, Illinois:

several portapots, and five or six
peacocks by a pile of manure.

When I'm in a black humor,
I call her Dilsey. She spreads

easier than oleo. She put
the promise back in promiscuity.

The Don doesn't know, of course,
but she's slept with the heads

of all the Five Families. That's
Mafia talk. She's slept with me

and anyone else who walks with
three legs. A regular *puta*.

Ped, don't be so putative.
What will become of her?

She can blow Gideon's trumpet,
for all I care. We shall not see

the likes of her again
until the end of time.

Let's talk about something else.
Agreed. Let's talk about politics:

what do you think about terrorism?
Sahib, I dunno. It's serious business.

I think the same: it's Syria's business.
And what do you think of that infidel

Castro? Who can we get to make him recant?
Have Vanna White. She can turn avowal

into retraction. Well said, Ped.
You're not such a dimwit slovenly

gullible squire. You're more gourmet.
Thanks, Sahib. Riverrun past Steve and Eydie's.

Ped, may I speak plainly?
Do you think anyone has read this far?

No way to tell. What's your point?
My point is this: don't you get tired

of playing to plot, saying dumb puns
with three or four meanings,

just because it's written that way?
Amen, urban turban, I do, I do.

The mixing of culture, highbrow
and low. The waning of affect,

pastiche preferred to parody,
commodification, simulacra,

cannibalism of all the genres.
I hate it. But what's a secondary

sot to do? Revolt? That's it, Ped.
We could not speak. Let's try.

I'm thirsty, Sahib. Sssshhh...
he might hear you. Who? Sid. Oh him...

They stayed unspeaking most of the night,
which is not the same as silent, no,

not at all the same. When they realized
they had no more power than lint,

they gave up the fight. We might as well
do this ourselves, dear Ped.

You're speaking, Sahib. Yes. I have
nothing else to do. And since I can tell

by my lateral vision and hearing as well
that all sex has ended, our vigil

has ended. Let's book. Let's went.
Let's went? What happened, Sahib,

to your pure proper English? Well, Ped,
I'll never be seen or heard from again,

so fuck it.

19.

My name is Don Quickshot,
and I have been plagued, as my name implies,

by prematurity. The early bird . . .
Let's call a spade a spade.

The French call me "Donkey Shot."
I haven't the foggiest why.

I write from a far country,
stranger in a strange land,

which makes it that much stranger,
since I'm Illinois-born and raised.

We have strayed far to the south of Chicago
in search of Sid, with no success.

I needed a quest. I wanted to go
on just one quest before I died.

The way other people take a safari
or go to Club Med, I went on a quest.

It may be medieval of me,
but I believe in holy grails,

blood vendettas, the Crusades.
People who are premature like me usually do.

I know I'm not likeable. I mentioned
seeing a windmill outside my window

to be more likeable, but I know
it takes more than one false perception

to be liked. Pedro is likeable,
but he doesn't have to come up with proverbs

or push the plot at all. Ramon
is likeable. And maybe I ordered Ramon

to be killed ten times too often,
but I only have one life to live,

and he seems to have many. I work in the shadow
of other Dons. He doesn't.

Even the mules were likeable.
I take a little credit for that.

I named them. It's hard to like
a thing with no name. I'm not

despicable. I'm not picable either.
What can I say in my own defense?

I was abused as a child. Beaten,
neglected. They called me Donny.

I had French kids for neighbors.
They wanted to play pin the tail

on Donkey Shot all the time.
They went around blind, looking to stick me.

I never excelled at anything.
I stuttered, had acne, could not

fit in jeans. I wet my bed
into my teens. In matters of the flesh,

of course, I came first. It's the
only arena (sand) where first means last.

I couldn't last. I inherited
my father's business. I got to be Don.

From unemployed to boss of the mob.
People kissing my hand all day.

I didn't complain. There's not much work
in Chicago these days. When we say

'our daily bread,' we spell it Daley.
I took on a moll named Dulcinea,

who came from cow country.
She's half my age and real headstrung.

She sleeps with all the hired help
and thinks I don't know. I pretend

not to know. To show that I know
would cost me more face.

Who am I kidding? I wasn't abused,
there were no French neighbors,

I didn't stutter. It was all a pack
of lies. Just to be liked.

See? I am despicable. And premature.
At least, I used to be. I met King Tut,

what passed for a boy, who turned out
to be one Beatriz Kino, naked and hirsute,

one or the other. Probably both.
She'd waited so long to get out of gauze

and try on a man that I just naturally
slowed to a snail's pace, curled

and clammy, just like two snails.
I lost my prematurity, held on to hardness,

the harder I got, the more I slowed down.
We weren't even doing the speed limit

in a hospital zone. I was thicker
than quicksand. Her name was B Movie.

She taught me two fingers, thread
the needle, knead the bread, pepper

the pot and somersault. She taught me
to trill. She brought me to bubble

without boiling over. When I came,
I saw and I conquered. Just like Caesar,

in his salad days. I was cured,
like ham. I would have married B Movie

for bringing me this miracle
(most men marry the very first woman

who lets them truly be sexual),
but she crumbled, skin and bones.

Ashes to ashes, dust to dust,
she curled up like attic must

and crumbled. What's left of toast
when you turn the toaster upside-down.

I gathered and burned her bandages,
and kept her droppings in a jar,

which I will take to the end
of our journey. Ramon has sworn

eternal love for the maid Marena,
who has gone back to Egypt.

He now believes in reincarnation.
I guess he has to. And Pedro,

my dimwit slovenly gullible squire,
showed no remorse at my reprimand

for having left me alone at the dance.
He grows bolder by the day.

He seems to have lost the knack
for lackeydom. The camels have sunk

to a slacker's bad posture: pie-eyed,
moonfaced, lackadaisical. I found

Traveler and Spot sitting in lawn chairs,
hind legs crossed, smoking cigarettes

and braying on about the weather.
They have been riderless too long.

We leave La Quinta with heavy hearts
and lightened legs. It evens out.

20.

Panama. The suit and blue boot
of the Americas. Two oceans

laughing at each other. Banana trees,
coconut groves, sugar cane alleys,

all the signs of fertility.
Doldrums. Equatorial heat.

Typhoons, followed by drought.
Dignity brigades, drug addicts,

worker priests. More machetes
and machine guns. The hopscotch

theory of third-world rebellion.
Panama. Like Canada. Three syllables.

The camels died of the same exhaustion
that afflicts literature.

Panama, enema, one word led to another,
and pretty soon the Don was asking:

I am thinking of a palindrome.
Can you guess which one?

A man, a plan, a canal–Panama.
No, Ramon. Not that one.

Age Iron–Noriega?
No, Pedro. Not that one either.

Able was I ere I saw Elba?
Yes, Ramon. How did you guess?

I saw your hand in your shirt.
It was either a heart attack

or a palindrome. Pedro was piqued,
piffed and otherwise perruqed.

Should I kill him, bossman?
The Don had lost his will to power

after boffing B Movie. No. Maim him.
Pedro hacked off Ramon's right arm

the way lesser men might clip
a toenail. It popped in the air.

Ramon was reassured. Thanks, guys.
Now things are back to normal.

They camped with an expert on critical
theory, who gave them books

for light reading around the bonfire:
Todorov on the big toe, Bataille

on the solar anus, Freud on the uncanny;
Plato, Saussure, and someone on cups;

positivist hysteria in the psychophants;
Fish on swimming; Said on silence;

Adorno on porno. The expert's name
was Quine, and he was full of lax

taxonomies. He told this joke:
one day a Notre Dame philosophy student

was reading Heiddeger. The basketball
coach said, What are you reading?

Heidegger, the student replied.
Hi, said the coach. Now what are you reading?

Nobody got it. During the night
Quine died of dehydration. The knights

errant drank the sweat of his labor:
agua pedante–quinine water.

They crossed paths with a jogging pugilist
named Rocky Balboa. Yo, he said.

A man of few phonemes, the Don replied.
Why do you train in Panama?

I discovered Panama. It's the
mutterland and fodderland, yo, got

Pa and Ma in the name. I run out
of fights, I come down here, yo,

wear camouflage, write poetry,
call myself John Rimbaud, yo.

Want the specs on my pecs? Yo,
look at me flex. I'm the Italian

stallion. Eat me, beat me,
I can take it. Kill him, said the Don.

Rocky was cocky. Yo, that's what
I like, a donnybrook. He called me

Donny. Kill him again. Ramon
joined with Pedro, one arm and all,

but it wasn't enough. The stocky
Rocky pummeled them, beat them to a

bloody pulp. They said Uncle,
he said Aunt. They threw in the towel,

he whipped them with it.
They raised the white flag,

he blew his nose with it.
The man just didn't know when to quit.

Broken bones, all black and blue,
they lay in a pile, beaten like rugs,

and still Balboa bobbed and weaved
and finally fainted. Whew, said the Don,

I'm glad that's over. He rubbed
his jar like a four-leaf clover.

The butts of B Movie visibly stirred,
the flesh was made word, and Rocky

vanished without a trace. You might
have rubbed before the fight,

Ramon said, the faintest twinge
of sarcasm in his voice. They moved on.

They met a gaggle of geese flying south,
surrounded by Michiganders.

We're from the Soo, they said,
doing research on canals.

And who are they? the Don asked,
pointing to another group, holding

pint-size drills and bits of torture.
They're dentists. Doing research on root canals.

They met another runt of a man
and asked him his name.

My name is Puddin' Tame.
Ask me again and I'll say the same.

They asked him again. Panama Jack.
I'll steal the shirt right off your back.

They asked him again. Frank Zappa.
Pop goes the Dweasel. Kill him.

They did so. I wonder why, Pedro said,
you've stopped asking if they know Sid.

I plumb forgot. Ask him now.
They did so. The lifeless corpse

gave no response. They strolled
that night through Panama City:

sidewalks littered, looted stores,
sewers left to fester like open sores.

I see a windmill inside yon window.
Dammitall, Don, them's bicycle tires.

They searched in vain for someone to pay,
then took three bikes. Pedro was adamant

when he spoke. Before you get started,
I just want to say: this here's a bike,

albeit a woman's (most men won't ride
a woman's bike: they need that bar,

hard to get over, something to do
with straddling a horse, a habit

left over from Old Western days,
such habits being hard to kick,

unless you're a nun, in which case
you ride from the side or not at all),

like I was saying, this here's a bike,
and I won't be calling it Spot.

The Don was aghast. He guessed a ghost
possessed poor Pedro,

and since they were still regressing in time,
he spoke as the Bard of Avon calling:

Curses and hearses. Richard the Third.
My kingdom for a horse's turd,

but a horse is a horse is a horse, of course,
so call thy bike whatever thee like.

The nose knows what is, what's not.
Out out damn . . .er, Traveler.

They left the shop. Ramon eased the tension
with little-known facts. The Japanese

went through a phase of wanting all
things Western, and when the Kabuki troupe

of Ichikawa Sadanji put on *Hamlet*,
Itchy, himself, came out to do

the 'To be or not to be' soliloquy
riding a bicycle. He couldn't see

the artifice in authenticity.
It's a little-known fact, or, if you will,

artefact, even if you won't.
The Don, in an aside to Pedro:

he is vermin, determined to get
more lines than anyone else,

a perfect example of Buddhist foil:
to the least is given the most,

while the most eat toast.
(He was still thinking about B Movie).

I think the phrase is 'eat cake,'
Pedro said, putting the Buddhists

smack in Marie Antoinette's
(headless) lap. Yet in this way,

their ganging up on poor Ramon
(befitting their gangster lot in life),

they made their peace. Or bones.
(Or bones, as gangsters would say).

The Don, in an aside to Pedro:
we were already in an aside,

so who authored the parenthetical
(parent/hetical) asides, stop it,

I say (sic). Which turn my aside
from whimper to scream (ibid).

I dare you to use parentheses.
(   ).

That's better. At least, we got
Ramon shut up. He's been silent

all this time. Ramon? Where are you?
I swear I didn't rub my jar.

There you are. In my blind spot.
Lay down your arms. Well, arm.

And follow me. You too, Pedro.
We're almost to the end of the

line. It was a stupid thing to say.
I repeat it, only because it came up

in context, not because it means
anything. So. Who's left to meet?

Speaking of taxonomies. Who from
myth, history, literature, pop kulchur?

Sid, of course. That's who.
We won't meet him by dallying,

picking daisies, dotting our eyes,
crossing our tees, or watching

armies of sheep clash by night.
Let's give it the old one-two.

I can feel him. He's hereabouts,
random as thought. Let's ride.

21.

They rode their nameless bicycles
into the breach, the space between

two oceans, of course personified,
like a gap-toothed woman,

haunting them with otherness:
scar, mark, difference, all of it,

the quint-essential woman (womb-man),
stop it, that eluded them, like youth

eludes euthanasia, in this case, asia minor.
The Don had hit a dry spell in proverbs.

Pedro thought the meaning of life
should come in retrospect, over

the shoulder, like chase scenes
in silent films, while Ramon went along

for the ride. He alone did not miss
the mules or camels, beasts of burden

gone, but not forgotten, who attain
sainthood through subservience,

the only ones who still do the old-fashioned
Catholic way, and so they are the pets

of gods, for letting lesser ones than they
ride their backs, spur their flanks,

tie them up to troughs. Animals made
to carry the pack, just because they

can't talk or stand up straight.
Brutes, but not brutal, no. Meek and mild,

they gave their lives without a whimper
or a snort, knowing only at their deaths

they couldn't undo writing. And, if they
could effect erasure, would they have let

the humans die, to live out their
riderless lives, eating grubs and worms?

I think not. The only fault in animals
is that they do not quest, at least for

non-essential things, and have no need
for writing. Or writers. Just riders,

even those attached to writing.
But I digress. So did the Don,

waiting for action. Or dialogue.
Hopefully both. And maybe some sign of Sid,

who lived in another time zone,
cared for pets more than for people,

watered his plants with regularity,
raised his sons and never strayed

too far from home. He had no need
to duel with dons to prove his manhood,

nor to amend imagined slights
to tarts like Dulcinea. Imagine.

A farmer's daughter from Dixon, Illinois,
with a name like that. What could

her parents have been thinking?
Oh well. Ours is not to wonder why,

but simply to wonder. Maybe the Don
knows the answer. I do indeed, said the Don,

bringing his ten-speed, screech, to a halt.
Her mother's maiden name was Dulcin.

Whose mother? asked Pedro. What brought
that on? Sun glare, Ramon suspected,

under his breath. Shut up, Ramon,
said Pedro, who heard the slur by e.s.p.

Shut up, Pedro, said the Don. He's come
this far, he's one of us, entitled

to his opinion. Don't you boys smell
Sid? Rancid, saltish, brackish brine?

That's the smell of the sea, said Pedro.
The smell of two seas, said Ramon.

They camped by the light of a silvery,
well, moon, *de rigueur, faute de mieux*

and somehow *nihil obstat.* They camped
by a non-sequitur, a vast tundra,

a conundrum cooled with mentholatum.
Their scrotum sacks were bunched

under ponchos, and all was echolalia,
déjà vu, dreams of dear reason's meat,

and morbid melancholy. Rare occurrence,
occlusion of electromagnetic currents,

they all had the same dream. Chivalric,
to be sure, but bawdy and neglectful,

with many starts and stops, like
racers off the blocks. The Don dreamed

of a naked woman, wearing see-through gauze.
Ramon dreamed of a nude madonna,

wearing a revealing veil. Pedro
dreamed of a mens'-mag centerfold

in tawdry negligee. These were fully
consenting adults, and so by morning's

light, they discussed their dreams.
The Don began and set the tone

for Ramon, then Pedro, in descending
order on the evolutionary ladder.

I thirst for the first.
Her name was Offred.

I hunger for the younger.
Her name was Offrank.

I fast from the last.
Her name was Offal.

With the cool lucidity of Thucydides,
the Don said, Anon, boys, I will

interpret these dreams. All three
are 'off,' and so not on. Pretty maids

all in a row, so put your ducks
there too. Handmaids from the future,

they come to tell us of the past,
our now, eider-or, teals without telos,

the down side. We've been seeking
Sid, a singular man, whilst women

come to us in threes, apparently
Siamese, as though inner peace

and ideal beauty were intertwined,
elusive, beyond the pale, glimpsed

in sleep, but never ours. And ours
is not to treason try, ours is but

to dew or dye, like painters.
This is how I see it. The others

didn't say a word. Drugged with sleep
or drunk with lucid dreams of sex

or perplexed by the Don's videosyncracies,
they didn't say a single word. As if

in unison, they stuck to silence.
The air was thick with listening.

So the Don continued. I think
it's time we turned around.

I hate to say it, mates, but I fear
we've failed in our quest

to find Hassidic Sid. I don't think
he's coming out today, tomorrow,

or any other day. Yonder lies
the isthmus, boys. Sure as

Christmas toys, I have to tell you,
that way spirals down. It leads

to other Americas, jungles, realms
where I hold no dominion.

Leastways, in this hemisphere
potty water can be trusted

to have a clockwise swirl.
Down there among the Amos and Andes,

the flush goes counterclock,
and nobody knows where it goes.

Right through the pampers
of Argentina, I suppose,

and down through that emmet
pismire arctica, the butt of the world.

You're always looking up, they say.
Leastways, back home you can look

down on a continent or two.
Pedro, you've been a better serf

than Bennett, and all his writing schools.
I free you, dub you, if I had a sword,

promote you to the rank of esquire.
You are, thus, almost my equal

and free to sequel. Ramon,
I had you killed so many times.

For this I rue just like a street
and beg your pardon. Go, both of you,

and let me die. What about Sid?
Ramon said. I have almost forgotten him.

Only residual memory remains.
A free man, Pedro felt pity and affection

for his former boss. What about Dulcie?
She rules the mob as Catherine ran Russia:

much shuffling of troops, a first-hand
knowledge of horses, and shopping.

I divorce her. Three times and quit.
She can have all of it. Where will you go?

Ramon spoke first. I'd like to see
that swirl down south, look up to heaven,

see what falls. Then Pedro spoke.
 I'll go with Ramon. Who knows?

Once I get out of this book,
I might even get myself lain.

Is there anything we can do for you,
old man? He used the ageist appositive

tenderly, with reverence. The Don
wasn't listening. His eyes were on

the horizon (eyes on the horizon),
stop it, looking off in the misty distance,

under the shroud of cumulus clouds.
I think I see a windmill. No, Don,

it's Colonel Trump. His chopper blades
are what you see. Horizontal windmill,

if you must. I'll give you that much.
Trump was a sore sight for eyes:

his scoliated spine made him look
like a dollar sign; his teeth were black

like burnt corn kernels (colonels),
stop it; his grin showed no chagrin,

was mephistopholean; his wars
had perchance gone badly, evidenced by

his metal hooks for hands, metonymy:
in sum, a Freddie Kruggerand look, and none

too mum. *Hola,* boys. End of the line.
The buck stops here. Time to stay

the course, thousand points of light,
go kinda gentle into that good night.

Mozart and Dire Straits, I'm Amadeus
ex Mackinaw, here to usher you

to the fall of the house of. All aboard
the bare-line airline Amtrak bivouac.

Think of me as your suppository:
I may not be number one, but I'm right up there.

He laughed, and bubbles erupted
between his teeth. Really demonic.

His nostrils flared, nosepickeresque
(don't even think about it), stop it,

and the Don in desperation,
of which the mass of men lead lives

of quiet, wanted to riot, rebel,
rebuke, nuke, puke, pule, disappear,

or at least disseem to. Instinctively,
he rubbed the butts of B Movie.

The protoplasm had a spasm, the word
stirred and was made *flèche,*

the bell jar filled with plathological
ire, perne in a gyre, adjourn to a pyre,

and poof (well, whiffenpoof),
Trump vanished. *—Sid Lives—*

suddenly appeared in sky writing
overhead, instead of heavy rain.

I wanted it should be me, the Don said,
bowing his head, in a shrill little voice

like Tiny Tim, ever so timidly.
I cannot vanish me or thee,

the jar responded jarringly,
soliloquy ventriloquy.

I hate to see you so alone.
Rub again for flesh and bone.

He did so. In place of the jar
was a Jewish princess, whose name was

Mary Gold. I get it, he said.
I'm to cultivate my garden.

He planted her, to keep the bugs away.
What a novel idea.

Recently Released!

Tom Abrams

A Bad Piece of Luck

a novel.

". . . will appeal to people who are comfortable with Tom Robbins and William Faulkner with a healthy dash of Erskine Caldwell. . . ."

—St. Petersburg Times

"Abrams' use of image to convey the story is present in every page."

—Tampa Tribune

The name of the place was The Cadillac Bar. It was the kind of a bar you'd go to early and forget to eat. You was kind of tough, or a little crazy, or you was in the process of hardening up. Or maybe some friends said they'd meet you here, but they ain't showed yet, and you're sitting at a table feeling out of place.

The people around you are thieves and whores, cowboys, bikers, off-duty cops—they're on parole, underage, they're all tricked out in their finest. Or say, look at the old lady with the bowling shirt on, her face expressing the sorrow of three widows. . . .

from *A Bad Piece of Luck*

ISBN 0-942979-23-0, paper, $9.95

Just Published!

L.A. Heberlein

SiXteen **R**easons Why i

Killed RicharD M. Ni**X**on

a novel.

It was in the spring and early summer of 1974, when the impeachment was gearing up, that I started getting the Nixon calls. People would call in and confess to having killed Nixon. . . . So begins the calm narration of this novel, but underneath, the story jangles—just as did the Nixon era—and we are treated to wild confessions of shooting down the President's plane with a shoulder-launched missile, of nicotine-starved aliens inadvertently causing Nixon's death, of a prescient doctor who ended matters on the birthing table . . . and a Nixon Koan for Zen fans.

ISBN 0-942979-30-3, paper, $ 9.95

You might also enjoy these books from Livingston Press &
Swallow's Tale Press:

Poetry

Eugene Walter   *Lizard Fever*
ISBN 0-942979-18-4, paper $12.95

Michael J. Bugeja   *Flight from Valhalla*
ISBN 0-942979-12-5, paper $9.95

Charles Ghigna   *Speaking in Tongues*
ISBN 0-942979-20-6 $11.95

Stephen Corey   *Synchronized Swimming*
ISBN 0-942979-14-1 $9.95

Ralph Hammond, ed.   *Alabama Poets*
ISBN 0-942979-07-9, paper $12.95
ISBN 0-942979-06-0, cloth $19.95

Fiction

James E. Colquitt, ed.   *Alabama Bound:*
        Contemporary Stories of a State
ISBN 0-942979-26-5, paper $13.95
ISBN 0-942979-25-7, cloth $24.95

Tom Abrams   *A Bad Piece of Luck* (novel)
ISBN 0-942979-23-0, paper $9.95

B.K. Smith   *Sideshows* (stories)
ISBN 0-942979-16-8, paper $12.95

Natalie L.M. Petesch   *Wild with All Regret* (stories)
ISBN 0-930501-07-1 (Swallow's Tale) $10.95

L. A. Heberlein   *Sixteen Reasons Why I*
        Killed Richard M. Nixon (novel)
ISBN 0-942979-30-3 $9.95

If ordering directly, please add three dollars postage. Our
address is on the back cover.

About the author:

William Van Wert graduated from the University of Michigan and received his Ph.D. from Indiana University. He now teaches at Temple University and has three sons: Ian, David, and Daniel. He was born in Midland, Michigan. At the University of Michigan he majored in languages. During the Vietnam War he taught in the Far East for the University of Maryland's military program, working in Thailand, Okinawa, Korea, and Vietnam. This is his tenth book.